Weight Watchers®

D0376015

easy meals with meat

Sue Ashworth

SIMON & SCHUSTER
A VIACOM COMPANY

First published in Great Britain by Simon & Schuster, 1998
A Viacom Company

This edition produced for
The Book People Ltd
Hall Wood Avenue
Haydock
St Helens
WA11 9UL

First published 1998
Reprinted 2002

Simon & Schuster UK Ltd
Africa House
64–78 Kingsway
London WC2B 6AH

Front cover design: Zoocity
Typesetting: Stylize Digital Artwork
Photography: Steve Lee
Styling: Marian Price
Food preparation: Wendy Lee

ISBN 0 68484 043 X

Printed in Hong Kong

Recipe notes:
Egg size is medium, unless otherwise stated.
Vegetables are medium-sized, unless otherwise stated.
It is very important to use proper measuring spoons, not cutlery, for spoon measures.
1 tablespoon = 15 ml; 1 teaspoon = 5 ml
Dried herbs can be substituted for fresh ones, but the flavour may not always
be as good. Halve the fresh-herb quantity stated in the recipe.

Contents

Introduction

So you're trying to lose weight, you're trying to eat healthily and you're probably trying to cater for the tastes of others too. Not an easy task, especially when time is at a premium. This is where *Easy Meals with Meat* comes in handy. It has been written just for you, with a modern approach to the demands of today's lifestyles.

Why spend hours in the kitchen when you have a hundred and one other jobs to do? (Besides, it's hardly the best place to be when you are on a diet.) When time is tight and your family is hungry, you need to have a ready repertoire of ideas to call upon to produce nutritious, tasty food that everyone will enjoy. British Meat and Weight Watchers have come up with some answers. In *Easy Meals with Meat* you will find lots of recipes for healthy, well-balanced food which is ready in minutes.

With Weight Watchers *1, 2, 3 Success Plus*™ losing weight is easy, and you get oodles of moral support! The simple Points system helps you to eat healthily by keeping the saturated fat intake low and encouraging you to eat lots of fresh, healthy fruit and vegetables. Weight Watchers helps you get the balance right.

The recipes in *Easy Meals with Meat* are perfect for Weight Watchers Members. Why? Because they're low in fat and therefore low in Points and Calories. The first step is to choose lean, trimmed cuts of meat, and that's easy to do now since there's far more choice these days at your local butcher or supermarket. For some recipes you may have to add some fat – some oil for stir-frying for example – be sure to use as little as you can get away with; our recipes keep fat to the bare minimum. Finally, it's important to choose your cooking method carefully – dry-frying, stir-frying, grilling, barbecuing, microwaving, roasting on a trivet, and casseroling are all ideal for a weight-loss programme.

The recipes in this handy book make the most of readily-available ingredients. You may find a few items that you haven't come across before, but you should be able to buy them from your local supermarket. (It's surprising what's there when you look for it!) Where possible, we give alternatives for anything which may not be widely available.

All the recipes in *Easy Meals with Meat* have been Calorie-counted, and they have been allocated Points so that you can fit them into your fantastic *1, 2, 3 Success Plus*™ programme, so why not give them a try? Many of the recipes are every bit as delicious with pork, lamb or beef – the choice is yours. So just flick through the pages to find a tasty recipe – it will be on the table in no time at all!

Ten helpful tips

- Look for trimmed cuts of meat, or those labelled 'extra-lean' or 'lean' and meat products labelled 'low-fat'.
- Before you cook the meat, trim off any fat you can see.
- Try not to add any unnecessary extra fat or oil to a recipe, though sometimes you do need a little for stir-frying, for example. Instead of cream, use low-fat yogurt, fromage frais or half-fat crème fraîche.

- Remember that red meat is one of the best sources of easily absorbed iron in the diet – it is important for maintaining healthy blood. Red meat is also an important source of zinc as well as B vitamins (especially thiamin [B1], riboflavin [B2], niacin [B3], vitamin [B6] and vitamin [B12]).
- Meat is a very important source of protein – it is necessary for the healthy growth, maintenance and repair of our bodies.
- Eat your food slowly, putting your knife and fork down frequently, and savour every mouthful. You'll enjoy your meals more, they'll last longer and you won't get indigestion!
- When time is tight, choose meat that has been partially prepared – stir-fry strips, lean cubed meat, trimmed steaks or lean or extra-lean mince, for instance.
- Keep the balance right in your diet by eating lots of fresh fruit and vegetables (aim for 5 portions a day).
- Make sure you have your fair share of starchy energy-providing foods such as potatoes, rice, bread, pasta, beans, grains, noodles and cereals.
- Try to get into the habit of having a large mixed salad (with fat-free dressing) with at least one meal a day.

Lamb

When you want fast, easy meals with lots of flavour, you can really rely on lamb. With such a wide range of tasty trimmed cuts to choose from in the supermarket or at your local butcher, you simply can't go wrong; the only problem you might have is making up your mind! To help you choose, have a quick look through the recipes on the following pages to spark your imagination and fire up your taste-buds. Then just put on that apron and get cooking! With food like this, dieting is a pleasure, not a chore.

Lamb Steaks with Rosemary, Red Onion and Redcurrant Glaze

Lean lamb steaks are a real treat with this delicious glaze. Serve with lightly cooked fresh vegetables or a salad, adding the extra Points.

Serves: 4
Preparation time: 5 minutes + 15 minutes cooking
Freezing: not recommended
Points per serving: 4$^{1}/_{2}$
Total Points per recipe: 18
Calories per serving: 255

2 teaspoons olive oil
1 red onion, chopped finely
2 tablespoons redcurrant jelly
2 teaspoons chopped fresh rosemary or
    1 teaspoon dried rosemary
4 × 150 g (5$^{1}/_{2}$ oz) lean lamb leg steaks
salt and freshly ground black pepper
a few fresh rosemary sprigs, to garnish

❶ Heat the olive oil in a small saucepan and add the onion. Sauté over a low heat until the onion is soft, about 10 minutes. Add the redcurrant jelly and three or four tablespoons of hot water, stirring until the jelly has melted. Add the chopped or dried rosemary and season with salt and pepper.
❷ Preheat the grill. Arrange the lamb steaks on the grill pan and brush with the redcurrant glaze. Grill for about 5–6 minutes on each side or until

done, brushing frequently with the baste.
❸ Serve garnished with sprigs of fresh rosemary.

Variations: if you wish, add a clove of crushed garlic to the onion in step 1 for the final 3 minutes of cooking. You could also use fully trimmed lamb loin chops instead of lamb leg steaks. The Points per serving will be 7.

Spring Lamb Sauté with Steamed Vegetables

Succulent noisettes of lamb together with steamed new vegetables make a tasty, healthy dish.

Serves: 4
Preparation time: 10 minutes + 25 minutes cooking
Freezing: not recommended
Points per serving: 6
Total Points per recipe: 24
Calories per serving: 250

a bunch of spring onions, sliced
12 baby carrots, trimmed
6 small new potatoes, scrubbed and halved
4 small turnips, quartered
55 g (2 oz) frozen petit pois or garden peas
2 teaspoons olive oil
4 × 115 g (4 oz) lean lamb noisettes (boned, rolled and tied lamb cutlets)
1–2 garlic cloves, crushed
finely grated zest and juice of 1 small lemon
salt and freshly ground black pepper

1 Put the vegetables into a steamer and steam until just tender, about 10–15 minutes. Alternatively, cook them in a small amount of lightly salted boiling water until tender.

2 Meanwhile, heat the olive oil in a frying-pan and add the lamb noisettes. Cook over a high heat, turning once, for about 4 minutes. Add the garlic and lemon zest and cook for 2 more minutes on each side. Season with salt and pepper.

3 Just before serving, add the lemon juice to the lamb, bubbling it up until evaporated. Pile the vegetables on to 4 warmed plates, arrange the noisettes on top and serve.

Variation: if you can't find noisettes of lamb, use fully trimmed lamb cutlets instead. The Points will be the same.

Navarin of Lamb

Lean cubed leg of lamb cooked with onions, garlic, tomatoes, carrots and wine make this a tasty and warming dish.
Serve with mashed potatoes and swede, flavoured with plenty of chopped fresh parsley. Remember to add the
Points for the potato.

Serves: 4

Preparation time: 15 minutes + 20 minutes cooking

Freezing: recommended

Points per serving: 3½

Total Points per recipe: 14

Calories per serving: 250

2 teaspoons vegetable oil

450 g (1 lb) boned leg of lamb, fully trimmed and
    cut into cubes

1–2 garlic cloves, crushed

2 onions, sliced

2 celery sticks, sliced

2 carrots, sliced finely

1 heaped tablespoon paprika

8 plum tomatoes, skinned and chopped

1 tablespoon tomato purée

150 ml (5 fl oz) dry white wine

salt and freshly ground black pepper

To serve:

4 tablespoons low-fat plain yogurt

a few pinches of paprika

1 Heat the vegetable oil in a large, deep-sided frying-pan or wok. Add the lamb a handful at a time, cooking over a high heat to seal and brown (this will take about 5 minutes).

2 Add the garlic and onions, cook for 2 minutes and then add the celery and carrots. Stir well, then reduce the heat and cook gently for 5 minutes.

3 Add the paprika to the lamb mixture, stir well and then add the tomatoes, tomato purée and wine. Season with salt and pepper and cook for about

8 more minutes, until the vegetables are tender, and the lamb is cooked.

4 Serve the lamb with a tablespoon of yogurt on top of each portion and sprinkle with a little paprika.

Variation: use 400 g (14 oz) canned chopped plum tomatoes instead of fresh tomatoes if you prefer. Substitute 150 ml (5 fl oz) stock for the wine, if you prefer.

Lamb Chops with Orange, Mustard and Mint

This scrumptious marinade makes the most of delicious lamb chops.

Serves: 4

Preparation time: 10 minutes + marinating + 20 minutes cooking

Freezing: not recommended

Points per serving: 6½

Total Points per recipe: 26

Calories per serving: 405

4 × 115 g (4 oz) fully trimmed, extra-lean lamb chops
finely grated zèst and juice of 1 orange
1 tablespoon whole-grain mustard
1 tablespoon chopped fresh mint
225 g (8 oz) basmati or long-grain rice
salt and freshly ground black pepper
To serve:
a few fresh mint sprigs
thin strips of orange rind, to garnish

1 Put the lamb chops into a shallow dish. Mix the orange zest and juice with the whole-grain mustard, then mix in the mint and season with salt and pepper. Pour this mixture over the chops, turning them to coat. Cover and chill for at least 10 minutes and longer if possible.

2 Preheat the grill to a high temperature. Arrange the lamb chops on the grill rack and cook them for about 6–8 minutes on each side, until cooked, basting them from time to time with the remaining marinade.

3 Meanwhile, cook the rice in plenty of lightly salted boiling water until just tender – about 12 minutes. Drain well and divide evenly between 4 warmed serving plates. Arrange the chops on top and garnish with fresh mint sprigs and thin strips of orange zest.

Cook's note: try not to stir rice as it cooks; it will retain more of its flavour if you don't.

Tuscan Lamb

This recipe gives a robust, Italian flavour to lean, succulent lamb. Serve with rice and salad; remember to add the extra Points.

Serves: 4

Preparation time: 10 minutes + 30 minutes cooking

Freezing: not recommended

Points per serving: 3½

Total Points per recipe: 14

Calories per serving: 210

2 teaspoons olive oil
400 g (14 oz) lean leg steaks, trimmed and cubed
8 shallots or very small onions, peeled and halved
1–2 garlic cloves, crushed
3 celery sticks, sliced
150 ml (5 fl oz) lamb stock
125 ml (4 fl oz) red wine
8 plum tomatoes, skinned and chopped
12 stoned black olives, sliced (optional)
1 tablespoon capers
a few rosemary and sage sprigs, plus extra for garnish
salt and freshly ground black pepper

① Heat the olive oil in a large frying-pan and add the lamb cubes. Cook over a high heat for 3–4 minutes to seal and brown them.

② Add the shallots or onions, garlic and celery to the pan. Cook, stirring frequently, for a further 3–4 minutes, until the onion and celery have softened.

③ Add the stock, red wine, tomatoes, olives, if using, and capers to the pan. Add two or three sprigs of rosemary and sage. Cook for 15–20 minutes, stirring occasionally, until the lamb is tender and the liquid has been reduced by about one third.

④ Season with salt and black pepper and then serve garnished with fresh sprigs of rosemary and/or sage.

Cook's note: skinning tomatoes is easy if you put them in boiling water for a couple of minutes first. You could also use 400 g (14 oz) of canned plum tomatoes instead of fresh.

Succulent Lamb Steaks with Garlic and Thyme

Grilled lamb steaks are irresistible with a tasty garlic, lemon juice and thyme mixture. Serve with plenty of fresh, lightly cooked vegetables or a mixed salad.

Serves: 2
Preparation time: 5 minutes + 15 minutes cooking
Freezing: not recommended
Points per serving: 7
Total Points per recipe: 14
Calories per serving: 195

2 × 150 g (5¹/₂ oz) lean, trimmed lamb steaks
finely grated zest and juice of 1 lemon
2 garlic cloves, crushed
2 teaspoons fresh thyme leaves
salt and freshly ground black pepper
a few fresh thyme sprigs, to garnish

① Preheat the grill to high. Arrange the lamb steaks on the grill rack.

② Mix together the lemon zest and juice. Add the crushed garlic and thyme leaves. Season with a little salt and pepper.

③ Brush the lamb steaks with lemon juice baste, then grill them for about 6 minutes on each side, brushing them from time to time with the remaining baste.

④ To serve, garnish with a few sprigs of fresh thyme.

Cook's note: most lemons are sold with a fine wax coating to prevent loss of moisture. If you can find them, buy unwaxed ones. Otherwise scrub the lemons well before use.

Indian-spiced Lamb Kebabs

Serves: 4
Preparation time: 10 minutes + 15 minutes cooking
Freezing: not recommended
Points per serving: 5
Total Points per recipe: 20
Calories per serving: 170

450 g (1 lb) lean minced lamb
1 small onion, chopped finely

1 teaspoon cumin seeds
2 teaspoons ground coriander
1/2 teaspoon chilli powder
1 tablespoon lime or lemon juice
1 tablespoon chopped fresh mint
salt and freshly ground black pepper
a few fresh mint sprigs and lime or lemon
    wedges, to garnish

1 In a large bowl, mix together the lamb, onion, cumin seeds, coriander, chilli powder, lime or lemon juice and chopped mint. Season with salt and pepper.
2 Form the mixture into small meatballs and thread them on to kebab sticks.
3 Cook over hot coals or under a hot grill for about 15 minutes, turning once or twice until cooked through. Serve, garnished with a few fresh mint sprigs and some lemon or lime wedges.

Cook's note: soak wooden kebab sticks in water first to prevent them from burning; you could also wrap the tips with foil.

Indian Bread topped with Spiced Lamb

Serves: 4
Preparation time: 10 minutes + 15 minutes cooking
Freezing: not recommended
Points per serving: 7
Total Points per recipe: 28
Calories per serving: 390

2 teaspoons vegetable oil
450 g (1 lb) boned leg of lamb, fully trimmed
    and cubed

1 onion, chopped
2 tablespoons garlic pickle or 2 tablespoons balti
    curry paste
150 ml (5 fl oz) low-fat plain yogurt
10 cm (4-inch) piece of cucumber, chopped finely
2 tablespoons chopped fresh coriander
4 mini naan breads
salt and freshly ground black pepper

1 Heat the oil in a wok or large frying-pan. Add the lamb, a handful at a time, and cook over a high heat until sealed and brown (this takes about 5 minutes). Add the onion, reduce the heat slightly, and cook for 5 more minutes, stirring occasionally.
2 Stir the garlic pickle into the lamb mixture and season to taste. Cook for a few more minutes or until cooked. Meanwhile, mix together the yogurt, cucumber and coriander.

3 Warm the naan breads, either in a low oven, under the grill or in a toaster. Place on warmed plates and top with the lamb. Spoon some of the cucumber and yogurt mixture on to each portion.

Variation: use trimmed neck fillet for this recipe, if you prefer. The Points will be 7 1/2 per serving and the Calories will be 430 per serving.

Indian-spiced Lamb Kebabs
Indian Bread topped with Spiced Lamb

Lamb Keema

As this recipe shows, tasty lamb curry doesn't have to take hours to make.

Serves: 4

Preparation time: 15 minutes + 30 minutes cooking

Freezing: recommended (but not the salad)

Points per serving: 5½

Total Points per recipe: 22

Calories per serving: 320

350 g (12 oz) lean minced lamb
1 teaspoon cumin seeds or ground cumin
1 teaspoon ground coriander
6 shallots or 1 large onion, chopped
1 red pepper, de-seeded and chopped
115 g (4 oz) fine green beans, chopped
175 g (6 oz) mushrooms, sliced
425 g (15 oz) canned chick-peas, rinsed and drained
400 g (14 oz) canned chopped tomatoes
1 lamb stock cube, dissolved in 6 tablespoons hot water
2 level tablespoons garlic pickle
salt and freshly ground black pepper
For the Indian salad:
¼ cucumber, chopped very finely
3 tomatoes, chopped very finely
1 small red onion (or ordinary one), chopped very finely
2–3 tablespoons chopped fresh coriander, plus extra sprigs to garnish

❶ Heat a large saucepan and add the lamb mince in small handfuls, dry-frying it for about 3–4 minutes until sealed and browned. Add the cumin and ground coriander and cook for another minute.

❷ Add the shallots or onion, red pepper and green beans. Stir-fry for a few moments, then add the mushrooms, chick-peas, tomatoes, stock and garlic pickle. Bring to the boil, then cover and cook gently for about 25 minutes, stirring from time to time. Remove the lid for the final 10 minutes or so to allow the liquid to reduce a little, but make sure that the curry does not boil dry.

❸ Meanwhile, prepare the salad by mixing together the cucumber, tomatoes, onion and fresh coriander.

Season with salt and pepper, then cover and chill until ready to serve.

❹ Check the seasoning of the curry, adding salt and pepper to taste, if necessary. Ladle on to 4 warmed serving plates and top with spoonfuls of the Indian salad. Garnish with a few extra sprigs of fresh coriander.

Variations: make this curry with extra-lean pork or beef mince another time; it will taste every bit as good! The Points per serving with pork or extra-lean beef will be 4½.

Irish Stew with Parsley Dumplings

Light parsley dumplings add an authentic touch to this comforting stew without making it too heavy.

Serves: 4
Preparation time: 15 minutes + 40 minutes cooking
Freezing: recommended
Points per serving: 8^1/$_2$
Total Points per recipe: 34
Calories per serving: 405

1 teaspoon vegetable oil
4 × 115 g (4 oz) fully trimmed lamb cutlets
8 shallots or small onions, halved
2 celery sticks, chopped
1 large carrot, sliced
2 leeks, sliced
1 lamb stock cube, dissolved in 425 ml (³/₄ pint)
   boiling water
1 teaspoon dried mixed herbs
25 g (1 oz) pearl barley
2 small potatoes, peeled and halved
salt and freshly ground black pepper
For the dumplings:
85 g (3¹/₄ oz) self-raising flour
a pinch of salt
2 tablespoons chopped fresh parsley
2 tablespoons polyunsaturated margarine

1 Heat the oil in a flameproof casserole dish or saucepan. Pop in the cutlets and cook them over a medium-high heat for about 2 minutes on each side, to brown them.

2 Add the shallots or onions, celery, carrot and leeks to the casserole and sauté them for a couple of minutes. Add the stock, herbs and pearl barley. Season with salt and pepper. Bring to the boil, then cover and reduce the heat. Simmer gently for 20 minutes.

3 Meanwhile, make the dumplings. Sift the flour and salt into a bowl. Mix in the parsley, then rub in the margarine until the mixture resembles fine breadcrumbs. Add just enough cold water to make a soft, but not sticky, dough. Form into 12 tiny dumplings.

4 Add the dumplings and potato halves to the casserole or saucepan. Cover and cook for a further 15–20 minutes, or until the dumplings and lamb are cooked and the pearl barley is swollen and tender. Serve the casserole with three dumplings per portion.

Irish Stew with Parsley Dumplings

Beef

Fancy a tender, succulent steak? Whether it's a fillet, rump or sirloin, there's nothing quite like a juicy steak to make you feel satisfied – even more so when you're dieting and you want something tasty. No problem! With Weight Watchers' wonderful *1,2,3 Success Plus*™, all things are possible! Whatever the day of the week or the occasion, you'll find recipes to suit in this chapter.

Beef Catalan

With its wonderful flavours of garlic, onions, red wine, olives and sultanas, this dish is a little taste of Spain.
It doesn't take long to put together, but it does take a while to cook, so go and put your feet up!

Serves: 6
Preparation time: 10 minutes + 1½–2 hours
   cooking + 10 minutes resting
Freezing: not recommended
Points per serving: 6½
Total Points per recipe: 39
Calories per serving: with silverside of beef 380;
   with brisket 390

2 tablespoons vegetable oil
900 g (2 lb) silverside of beef or brisket
12 shallots, halved or 2 red onions, sliced
2 garlic cloves, crushed
1 beef stock cube, dissolved in 300 ml (½ pint)
   boiling water
150 ml (¼ pint) red wine
25 g (1 oz) sultanas or raisins
18 small stoned black olives
3 large potatoes, each cut into about 8 wedges
1 tablespoon fresh thyme leaves or 2 teaspoons
   dried thyme
2 teaspoons cornflour, blended with a little
   cold water
salt and freshly ground black pepper
a few fresh thyme sprigs, to garnish

1 Preheat the oven to Gas Mark 4/180°C/350°F. Heat 1 tablespoon of oil in a roasting dish or flameproof casserole on the hob and add the joint, searing it over a high heat for a few minutes to brown on all sides.

2 Add the shallots or onions and garlic. Cook for a minute or two, then add the stock, red wine, sultanas or raisins and olives. Cover with a lid or a tent of foil and transfer to the oven to braise for 1½–2 hours until tender.

3 To prepare the baked potato wedges, put the remaining oil into a large bowl and add the potatoes

and thyme. Season well with salt and pepper and then toss them to coat. Tip them into a separate roasting tin. Put them into the oven on the top shelf for the final 50 minutes of cooking time.

4 Lift the joint of meat from the roasting pan, cover with foil and allow it to rest for 10 minutes before carving. Meanwhile, stir the blended cornflour into the pan juices and heat on the hob, stirring constantly, until the sauce is smooth and thickened. Cook gently for a further minute or so.

5 Serve the meat with the potato wedges and spoon the sauce around them. Garnish with thyme sprigs.

Beef Catalan

Spaghetti Bolognese

Extra-lean minced beef and plenty of vegetables make this all-time favourite a nutritious and balanced meal.

Serves: 4

Preparation time: 10 minutes + 30 minutes cooking

Freezing: recommended (sauce only)

Points per serving: 5

Total Points per recipe: 20

Calories per serving: 425

350 g (12 oz) extra-lean minced beef
1 large onion, chopped finely
2 garlic cloves, crushed (optional)
2 celery sticks, sliced
1 large carrot, chopped
400 g (14 oz) canned chopped tomatoes
225 g (8 oz) mushrooms, sliced
1 teaspoon dried mixed Italian herbs
1 tablespoon tomato purée
150 ml ($^1/_4$ pint) beef stock
225 g (8 oz) quick-cook spaghetti
salt and freshly ground black pepper
4 teaspoons freshly grated parmesan cheese,
    to serve

❶ Dry-fry the minced beef in a large saucepan, adding it a handful at a time and cooking it until well browned. Keep the heat high so that it browns and sears the meat.

❷ Add the onion, garlic, celery and carrot. Reduce the heat slightly and cook for a further 2–3 minutes.

❸ Stir in the canned tomatoes, mushrooms, herbs and tomato purée. Add the stock and bring to the boil. Cover and reduce the heat. Simmer gently for 20 minutes, removing the lid after 10 minutes so that the liquid reduces slightly.

❹ Meanwhile, cook the spaghetti for about 3–4 minutes in plenty of boiling, lightly salted water until just tender.

❺ Check the seasoning of the mince, adding salt and pepper according to taste. Drain the spaghetti, divide evenly between 4 warmed serving plates and top with the minced beef mixture. Sprinkle each portion with 1 teaspoon of parmesan cheese. Serve at once.

Variation: don't forget that lean pork or lean lamb mince are also excellent in Bolognese sauce. The Points per serving with pork will be 5 and the Points per serving with lamb will be 6.

Quick Beef Chilli

This beef chilli is very quick – perfect for the family on a weekday.

Serves: 4
Preparation time: 10 minutes + 35 minutes cooking
Freezing: recommended
Points per serving: 5¹/₂
Total Points per recipe: 22
Calories per serving: 365

350 g (12 oz) extra-lean minced beef
1–2 garlic cloves, crushed
1 onion, chopped finely
1 small red pepper, de-seeded and chopped
1 small green pepper, de-seeded and chopped
115 g (4 oz) mushrooms, sliced
400 g (14 oz) canned chopped tomatoes
425 g (15 oz) canned mixed beans in chilli sauce
115 g (4 oz) long-grain rice
salt and freshly ground black pepper

1 Dry fry the minced beef in a large saucepan or frying-pan, sautéing briskly for 2–3 minutes, until browned.

2 Add the garlic, onion and peppers and cook, stirring, for a further 2–3 minutes.

3 Add the mushrooms, tomatoes and mixed beans in chilli sauce to the saucepan. Heat until just boiling and then reduce the heat. Partially cover and simmer for 20–30 minutes, stirring occasionally, until the chilli is cooked.

4 Meanwhile, cook the rice in plenty of boiling, lightly salted water for about 12 minutes, until tender. Drain well. Season the chilli with salt and pepper according to taste and serve with the rice.

Variation: if you can't find canned mixed beans in a chilli sauce, use canned mixed pulses instead. Rinse and drain them and add 1–2 teaspoons of chilli powder, according to taste.

Hungarian Beef Casserole

This delicious casserole takes a little while to cook, but it only takes 10 minutes to prepare!

Serves: 4
Preparation time: 10 minutes + 1³/₄ hours cooking
Freezing: recommended
Points per serving: 5
Total Points per recipe: 20
Calories per serving: 290

2 teaspoons vegetable oil
350 g (12 oz) very lean stewing steak, cubed
1 large onion, sliced
1 garlic clove, crushed
2 tablespoons paprika
400 g (14 oz) canned chopped tomatoes
1 tablespoon tomato purée
1 red pepper, de-seeded and chopped
1 yellow pepper, de-seeded and chopped
1 courgette, sliced
1 beef stock cube, dissolved in 450 ml (16 fl oz) hot water
4 potatoes, peeled and cubed
4 tablespoons skimmed milk
1 tablespoon cornflour, blended with a little cold water
salt and freshly ground black pepper
To serve:
4 tablespoons low-fat plain yogurt
paprika, for sprinkling
some chopped fresh parsley

1 Heat the oil in a large saucepan to a high heat. Add the beef, a handful at a time, to seal and brown the meat. Turn the heat down a little and then add the onion and garlic. Cook, stirring, for about 3 minutes, until softened. Add the paprika and stir well to coat the meat and onions.

2 Add the tomatoes, tomato purée, red and yellow peppers, courgette and stock to the saucepan. Bring to the boil, then reduce the heat. Cover and simmer for 1¹/₂ hours or until the meat is very tender. Check the level of liquid from time to time, adding a little extra water if necessary.

3 During the last 25 minutes, cook the potatoes in lightly salted boiling water until tender. Mash well, add the milk and beat until smooth.

4 Season the casserole with salt and black pepper. Add the blended cornflour and cook for a couple of minutes until thickened. Top each portion with one tablespoon of yogurt, sprinkled with paprika and chopped parsley. Serve with the mashed potatoes.

Rump Steak and Root Vegetable Stir-fry

Root vegetables taste fantastic in a beef stir-fry – just slice them finely so they cook quickly.

Serves: 4
Preparation and cooking time: 20 minutes
Freezing: not recommended
Points per serving: 4
Total Points per recipe: 16
Calories per serving: 210

2 tablespoons soy sauce
3 tablespoons orange juice
2 teaspoons creamed horseradish (optional)
2 teaspoons dark or light muscovado sugar
2 teaspoons cornflour
2 teaspoons stir-fry oil or vegetable oil
350 g (12 oz) lean rump steak, sliced thinly
1 large onion, sliced finely
1 leek, trimmed and sliced finely
115 g (4 oz) celeriac, cut into matchsticks
    (or use 3 celery sticks, sliced finely)
115 g (4 oz) swede or turnip, cut into matchsticks
2 carrots, cut into matchsticks
2 tablespoons chopped fresh coriander or parsley
$1/2$ teaspoon caraway or cumin seeds (optional)
salt and freshly ground black pepper

❶ Blend together the soy sauce, orange juice, horseradish (if using), sugar and cornflour. Set aside.
❷ Heat the oil in a wok or large frying-pan. Add the strips of beef to the wok or pan, a handful at a time, to seal and brown them. Stir-fry over a high heat for about 3 minutes.
❸ Add the onion, leek, celeriac or celery, swede or turnip and carrots to the wok or frying-pan. Stir-fry for a further 2–3 minutes so that the vegetables are just cooked, yet still crunchy.
❹ Stir the soy sauce mixture and add to the wok or frying-pan. Add the chopped coriander or parsley and caraway or cumin seeds (if using). Heat, stirring constantly for about 1 minute, until blended and slightly thickened. Season to taste with salt and pepper and then serve on warmed plates.

Variation: feel free to vary the vegetables in this recipe and try out some of your favourites. Celery, broccoli, cauliflower, butternut squash and mushrooms are all excellent.

Cajun Beef and Bean Burgers

Add a bit of fire and spice to beef burgers.

Serves: 4

Preparation time: 10 minutes + 15 minutes cooking

Freezing: recommended (after step 2 and before cooking)

Points per serving: 5

Total Points per recipe: 20

Calories per serving: 490

350 g (12 oz) extra-lean minced beef
1 small red onion, chopped very finely
$^1/_2$ small red pepper, chopped very finely
2 garlic cloves, crushed
1 tablespoon chopped fresh thyme, or
   1 teaspoon dried thyme
1 tablespoon chopped fresh oregano, or
   1 teaspoon dried oregano
1 teaspoon Cajun seasoning or mild chilli powder
a few drops of Tabasco sauce
115 g (4 oz) canned red kidney beans, rinsed
   and drained
1 small egg, beaten
salt and freshly ground black pepper
To serve:
4 medium (55 g/2 oz) burger buns
4 crisp lettuce leaves, shredded
2 tomatoes, sliced

1 In a large mixing bowl, combine all the burger ingredients together until well-blended. Alternatively, use a food processor or blender to mix the ingredients. Process them for about 10–15 seconds until thoroughly combined.

2 Shape the mixture into four large burgers.

3 Preheat the grill to medium-high. Place the burgers on the grill rack and grill for about 6–7 minutes on each side, until well-browned.

4 Serve on burger buns, topped with plenty of shredded lettuce and some sliced tomatoes.

Variations: for a change, try using canned mixed pulses instead of red kidney beans. You could also make these burgers with lean lamb or extra-lean pork mince. The Points per serving will be 6 with lamb, and 5 with pork.

Chinese Beef Soup

It doesn't take long to prepare and cook this wonderfully satisfying soup which is full of fresh tastes, lively colours and oriental flavours.

Serves: 4

Preparation time: 15 minutes + 20 minutes cooking

Freezing: not recommended

Points per serving: 2½

Total Points per recipe: 10

Calories per serving: 160

2 teaspoons stir-fry oil or vegetable oil

175 g (6 oz) lean rump steak, sliced very thinly

1 garlic clove, crushed

2 beef stock cubes, dissolved in 850 ml (1½ pints) hot water

1 teaspoon Chinese five-spice powder

1 leek, sliced finely

1 carrot, sliced into matchstick strips

6 spring onions, sliced finely

115 g (4 oz) mushrooms (oyster, shiitake or ordinary ones)

1 tablespoon chopped fresh coriander or chives

55 g (2 oz) rice noodles, thread egg noodles or long-grain rice

1–2 tablespoons soy sauce

salt and freshly ground black pepper

To serve:

1 teaspoon sesame seeds

a few fresh coriander sprigs or chopped chives

a few thin slices of red chilli or red pepper (optional)

1 Heat the oil in a large saucepan and add the strips of beef, cooking them over a high heat for about 2–3 minutes until browned on all sides. Add the garlic and cook for a few more seconds.

2 Pour in the stock and add the Chinese five-spice powder, leek, carrot, spring onions, mushrooms, coriander or chives and noodles or rice. Bring to the boil, then cover and reduce the heat. Simmer for 12–15 minutes.

3 Season the soup with soy sauce, salt and pepper and then ladle into warmed bowls. To serve, sprinkle with sesame seeds and garnish with fresh coriander or chopped chives and, if you wish, a few thin slices of red chilli or red pepper.

Cook's note: stir-fry oil is a blend of different oils, flavoured with ginger, sesame and garlic. It will add quite a bit of 'oomph' to your stir-fries and soups. If you can't find it, just use vegetable oil instead. Chinese five-spice powder is readily available in most supermarkets.

Seven-spiced Steak with Stir-fried Vegetables

Look out for Thai seven-spice seasoning on the spice racks at your local supermarket – it makes steaks taste great!

Serves: 4

Preparation time: 10 minutes + 10–15 minutes
   marinating + 15 minutes cooking

Freezing: not recommended

Points per serving: 3¹/₂

Total Points per recipe: 14

Calories per serving: 270

4 × 140 g (5 oz) fillet, sirloin or lean rump steaks
finely grated zest and juice of 2 limes or 1 lemon
3 tablespoons soy sauce
2 teaspoons Thai seven-spice seasoning
1 tablespoon stir-fry oil or vegetable oil
a bunch of spring onions, sliced finely
175 g (6 oz) oyster or ordinary mushrooms, sliced
1 red pepper, de-seeded and sliced finely
1 yellow or orange pepper, de-seeded and
   sliced finely
115 g (4 oz) Chinese leaves or Savoy cabbage,
   shredded
salt and freshly ground black pepper
To serve:
a few fresh coriander sprigs
lime or lemon wedges

❶ Put the steaks into a shallow dish. Mix together the lime or lemon zest and juice, soy sauce and seven-spice seasoning. Add a little salt and pepper and pour over the steaks, turning them to coat. Cover and leave in the refrigerator for 10–15 minutes to marinate.

❷ Preheat the grill to high. Arrange the steaks on the grill pan. If you like your steaks rare, grill them for about 2¹/₂ minutes on each side; for medium grill them 4 minutes each side; and for well done grill them 6 minutes each side. Baste them occasionally with the marinade.

❸ Meanwhile, heat the oil in a wok or large frying-pan and add the spring onions, mushrooms, peppers and Chinese leaves or Savoy cabbage. Stir-fry over a high heat for about 3–4 minutes until the vegetables are cooked but still crunchy. Tip in any remaining marinade and stir-fry the vegetables for another few moments. Season with salt and pepper.

❹ Divide the vegetables between 4 warmed serving plates and arrange the cooked steaks on top. Garnish with plenty of fresh coriander and lime or lemon wedges.

Variation: instead of using Thai seven-spice seasoning, try substituting the same amount of Chinese five-spice powder for a change.

Steak and Vegetable Kebabs

Cook these tasty kebabs on the barbecue in the summer or under the grill when it's cold outside. Either way, they are heavenly. Serve with a green salad.

Serves: 4

Preparation time: 10 minutes + marinating + 10–15 minutes cooking

Freezing: not recommended

Points per serving: 2¹/₂

Total Points per recipe: 10

Calories per serving: 170

350 g (12 oz) lean rump steak, cut into cubes

3 tablespoons teriyaki marinade or dark soy sauce

1 tablespoon tomato purée

a few drops of Tabasco or chilli sauce

1 red onion, cut into chunks

2 courgettes, sliced into chunks

8 small tomatoes

salt and freshly ground black pepper

1 Put the steak into a bowl and add the teriyaki marinade or soy sauce, tomato purée and Tabasco or chilli sauce. Season with a little salt and pepper and stir well. Cover and leave to marinate in the refrigerator for at least 10 minutes.

2 If you are using a barbecue, make sure that the coals are hot. Otherwise, preheat the grill to a medium-high heat.

3 To prevent wooden kebab sticks from burning, soak them in water. You could also wrap the tips with foil as an extra precaution against burning. Thread the cubes of meat on to 8 kebab sticks with

the chunks of onion and courgette, and small tomatoes and arrange them on the grill rack.

4 Cook the kebabs for about 10–15 minutes until cooked; turn them often and baste them from time to time with the remaining marinade.

5 Transfer the kebabs to serving plates.

Cook's note: teriyaki marinade is a thin, dark Japanese sauce which gives these kebabs a delicious flavour. It is readily available from your local supermarket or delicatessen. You could also use dark soy sauce for a change.

Tagliatelle with Mini Meatballs in Tomato Sauce

Treat yourself to an old favourite – pasta with meatballs.

Serves: 4

Preparation time: 15 minutes + 35–40 minutes cooking

Freezing: recommended (sauce and meatballs only)

Points per serving: 3

Total Points per recipe: 12

Calories per serving: 340

225 g (8 oz) extra-lean minced beef
1 small onion, chopped finely
1 garlic clove, crushed
2 teaspoons mixed dried Italian herbs
115 g (4 oz) button mushrooms sliced
300 ml (^{1}/$_2$ pint) passata (sieved plum tomatoes)
1 tablespoon tomato purée
a few fresh basil leaves, torn into shreds
1 beef stock cube, dissolved in 150 ml
   (^{1}/$_4$ pint) water
225 g (8 oz) tagliatelle
salt and freshly ground black pepper
a few fresh basil sprigs, to garnish

1 In a mixing bowl, combine the mince, onion, garlic and dried herbs. Season with salt and pepper and then form the mixture into tiny meatballs.

2 Heat a large non-stick frying-pan and add the meatballs, dry-frying them until lightly browned. Add the mushrooms and dry-fry them for a few moments. Then stir in the passata, tomato purée, basil leaves and stock. Heat until simmering and then cook gently for 25–30 minutes or until the liquid is reduced by about one-third. Stir occasionally.

3 Ten minutes before the end of the cooking time, cook the tagliatelle in plenty of boiling, lightly salted water. Cook until just tender, then drain and serve with the meatballs. Garnish with sprigs of fresh basil.

Variations: if you can't find passata, use 800 g (1 lb 12 oz) canned, chopped tomatoes instead. You could also try using spaghetti, or any other pasta shape, instead of tagliatelle.

Pork

Pork is such a versatile meat; it goes so well with different ingredients and can be prepared in so many ways. Lean strips of pork are the ideal choice for stir-fries you can put together in minutes. Pork mince is excellent for burgers, curries, pasta sauces and kebabs. Tender cubes of pork are just the cut for quick and tasty casseroles and succulent pork fillet or steaks are perfect for something a little special – not to mention one of the best stand-bys for no-nonsense mealtimes – trimmed pork chops. With the recipes in this chapter, one thing is for certain – you won't be stuck for choice!

Spiced Pork with Apricots

Dried fruits taste fantastic with pork. This dish combines sultanas and dried apricots with allspice and cumin for a wonderful Middle Eastern flavour. Serve with rice or noodles, remembering to add the Points.

Serves: 4
Preparation time: 10 minutes + 30–35 minutes cooking
Freezing: recommended
Points per serving: 4
Total Points per recipe: 16
Calories per serving: 245

1 tablespoon vegetable oil
450 g (1 lb) lean leg of pork, cubed
6 shallots, halved or 1 large onion, chopped
85 g (3 oz) ready-to-eat dried apricots, halved
25 g (1 oz) sultanas
1/2 teaspoon ground allspice
1/2 teaspoon cumin seeds or ground cumin
150 ml (1/4 pint) pork stock
2 teaspoons cornflour, blended with a little cold water
15 g (1/2 oz) pistachio nuts, chopped roughly (optional)

1 Heat the vegetable oil in a large frying-pan and add the pork, cooking over a high heat for a few minutes until sealed and browned. Add the shallots or onion and sauté for another 3–4 minutes.

2 Add the apricots, sultanas, allspice and cumin. Cook, stirring, for 1 minute.

3 Add the stock, then heat until simmering. Put the lid on and cook over a low heat for 20–25 minutes, until the pork is tender.

4 Stir the blended cornflour into the pork and cook, stirring, until thickened. Cook for another minute or so, then serve. Sprinkle with the pistachio nuts, if using.

Pork Medallions with Onion and Rosemary Rosti

Serves: 4
Preparation time: 10 minutes + 30 minutes cooking
Freezing: not recommended
Points per serving: $4^{1}/_{2}$
Total Points per recipe: 18
Calories per serving: 255

450 g (1 lb) potatoes, peeled and halved
1 small onion, chopped finely

1 teaspoon dried crushed rosemary
1 tablespoon olive or vegetable oil
450 g (1 lb) pork fillet, cut into 2 cm slices
2 tablespoons light soy sauce
2 red eating apples, cored and sliced but not
  peeled
2 tablespoons lemon juice
salt and freshly ground black pepper

❶ Parboil the potatoes in lightly salted water for about 8 minutes. Drain, cool for a few minutes and then grate them coarsely into a bowl (use a food processor for this if you prefer). Add the onion and dried rosemary, season and mix together.

❷ Heat the oil in a large frying-pan and place four mounds of the potato mixture in the pan, flattening the surface with the back of a spoon. Cook gently until browned underneath, then turn the rosti over carefully and cook the other side.

❸ Meanwhile, preheat the grill to medium-high and arrange the slices of pork fillet on the grill pan. Brush with the soy sauce and cook for 6 minutes on each side, turning them once and brushing with soy sauce on the other side. Place the sliced apple on the grill pan, brush with lemon juice and grill the apple with the pork for about 3 more minutes.

❹ Place the cooked potato rosti on to 4 warmed serving plates and arrange slices of the apple on top. Divide the slices of pork between the portions.

Pork Sausages with Sage, Apples and Cider

Serves: 4
Preparation time: 15 minutes + 25–30 minutes cooking
Freezing: not recommended
Points per serving: 6
Total Points per recipe: 24
Calories per serving: 290

2 teaspoons vegetable oil
1 large red onion (or an ordinary one), sliced

2 celery sticks, sliced
450 g (1 lb) low-fat pork sausages
2 teaspoons sage and apple seasoning or
  dried sage
2 apples, sliced
300 ml ($^{1}/_{2}$ pint) dry cider
1 pork stock cube, dissolved in 6 tablespoons
  hot water
salt and freshly ground black pepper

❶ Heat the vegetable oil in a large frying-pan and add the onion, celery and sausages. Cook over a medium heat for about 10 minutes, turning the sausages frequently, until they are browned.

❷ Add the sage and apple seasoning or dried sage. Add the apples, cider and stock. Simmer gently for about 15–20 minutes, until the liquid has been reduced to about half the amount.

❸ Check the seasoning, then serve.

Pork Medallions with Onion and Rosemary Rosti
Pork Sausages with Sage, Apples and Cider

Seasoned Pork Chops on a Bed of Leeks and Peppers

Tasty pork chops always make a satisfying meal. Here they are livened up with the fresh flavours of stir-fried leeks and pepper.

Serves: 2

Preparation time: 10 minutes + 25 minutes cooking

Freezing: not recommended

Points per serving: 7$\frac{1}{2}$

Total Points per recipe: 15

Calories per serving: 380

2 × 150 g (5$\frac{1}{2}$ oz) fully trimmed lean pork chops

1 tablespoon plain flour

2 teaspoons sage and apple seasoning

$\frac{1}{2}$ teaspoon celery seeds or a few shakes of celery salt

2 teaspoons vegetable oil

1 small onion, sliced

2 leeks, sliced

2 celery sticks, sliced

1 red pepper, de-seeded and chopped

1 pork stock cube dissolved in 300 ml ($\frac{1}{2}$ pint) hot water

salt and freshly ground black pepper

❶ Trim any fat from the pork chops.

❷ Sprinkle the flour on to a plate and add the sage and apple seasoning and celery seeds or celery salt. Season with salt and black pepper (or just black pepper if celery salt is used). Toss the pork chops in this mixture.

❸ Heat the vegetable oil in a frying-pan and add the onion, leeks and celery. Sauté for about 2 minutes, then add the red pepper and cook for another minute or so.

❹ Add the pork chops and stock to the pan, bring to the boil, then reduce the heat and simmer gently

for about 20 minutes. Turn the chops after the first 10 minutes. The dish is ready when the chops are cooked through and the vegetables are tender.

Cook's note: you can buy sage and apple seasoning in the supermarket: just look out for it on the spice racks. This blend of herbs and spices tastes just right with pork but if you can't find it, you can use dried sage instead.

Marinated Pork Fillet with Roasted Autumn Vegetables

Marinating a pork fillet and then roasting it with root vegetables and apples makes an easy, delicious meal.

Serves: 4
Preparation time: 10 minutes + 15 minutes marinating + 40–45 minutes cooking
Freezing: not recommended
Points per serving: 4½
Total Points per recipe: 18
Calories per serving: 260

5 tablespoons medium-dry sherry
2 tablespoons light soy sauce
2 teaspoons dried mixed herbs
1 tablespoon chopped fresh sage or parsley
450 g (1 lb) pork tenderloin (in one piece), trimmed of all visible fat
6 parsnips, sliced lengthways
450 g (1 lb) turnips or swede, cut into large chunks
2 apples
1 tablespoon lemon juice
salt and freshly ground black pepper

❶ In a large shallow dish, mix together the sherry, soy sauce, dried mixed herbs, sage or parsley and salt and pepper. Add the pork fillet to the dish with the marinade, turning to coat. Cover and leave to marinate in the refrigerator for about 15 minutes, turning occasionally.

❷ Preheat the oven to Gas Mark 6/200°C/400°F.

❸ Put the pork fillet into a roasting tin and arrange the parsnips and turnips or swede around it. Pour over any remaining marinade. Quarter and core the apples, without peeling them. Sprinkle the apple quarters with lemon juice and place next to the pork. Roast for 40–45 minutes until the pork is cooked and the fruit and vegetables are tender. It is not necessary to let the pork stand after cooking.

❹ Slice the pork and serve with the vegetables and apples.

Grilled Gammon Steaks with Fresh Tomato Chutney

This easy, tasty recipe is delicious served with fresh vegetables and accompanied by this spicy tomato chutney.

Serves: 2
Preparation time: 10 minutes + 20 minutes cooking
Freezing: not recommended
Points per serving: 5
Total Points per recipe: 10
Calories per serving: 245

2 × 115 g (4 oz) lean gammon steaks or fully trimmed bacon chops
2 teaspoons polyunsaturated margarine
1 small onion, chopped finely
1 small apple, chopped
15 g (½ oz) sultanas or raisins
a pinch of allspice or ground cinnamon
2 tomatoes, skinned and chopped
½ teaspoon dark or light sugar
a few drops of vinegar
salt and freshly ground black pepper

① Preheat the grill to high. Trim any fat from the gammon or bacon chops and arrange them on the grill rack.

② Melt the margarine in a small saucepan and sauté the onion until softened, about 3 minutes. Add the apple, sultanas or raisins, allspice or cinnamon, tomatoes and sugar. Add a little water, about 50 ml (2 fl oz), and bring to the boil. Cook for about 15 minutes until the liquid has reduced and the vegetables and fruit are soft and pulpy, stirring often. Season with a few drops of vinegar and add salt and pepper, according to taste.

③ While the chutney is cooking, grill the gammon steaks or bacon chops for about 4–6 minutes on each side. Serve accompanied by the fresh tomato chutney.

Pork, Tomato and Parsley Casserole

Lean pork cooked with lots of vegetables, canned tomatoes and plenty of fresh parsley make a tasty, oven-baked bean pot.

Serves: 4
Preparation time: 10 minutes + 35 minutes cooking
Freezing: recommended
Points per serving: 5$\frac{1}{2}$
Total Points per recipe: 22
Calories per serving: 345

350 g (12 oz) extra-lean pork mince
1 large onion, $\frac{1}{4}$ chopped finely, the
    remainder sliced
$\frac{1}{2}$ teaspoon ground ginger
2 tablespoons chopped fresh parsley
1 apple, peeled, cored and chopped
1 large carrot, sliced
1 turnip, chopped into small pieces
400 g (14 oz) canned chopped tomatoes
425 g (15 oz) canned mixed pulses, rinsed
    and drained
1 pork stock cube, dissolved in 300 ml ($\frac{1}{2}$ pint)
    boiling water
2 tablespoons tomato purée
1 tablespoon molasses sugar or dark
    muscovado sugar
1 tablespoon cornflour, blended with a little water
salt and freshly ground black pepper
some chopped fresh parsley, to garnish

① Put the pork mince into a mixing bowl. Add the finely chopped onion, ground ginger and parsley. Season with salt and pepper, mix well and form into small meatballs.

② Heat a large flameproof casserole dish or saucepan and add the meatballs, dry-frying them for about 3 minutes until sealed and browned.

③ Remove from the heat and add the remaining sliced onion, apple, carrot and turnip to the meatballs. Stir in the tomatoes, mixed pulses, stock, tomato purée and molasses or muscovado sugar. Stir well and season with salt and pepper.

④ Return to the heat and bring to the boil. Reduce the heat, then cover and cook gently for 30 minutes.

⑤ Add the blended cornflour and heat, stirring, until thick and glossy. Cook for 2 minutes and then ladle into warmed serving bowls. Sprinkle with chopped parsley and serve at once.

Sautéed Lemon and Ginger Pork

There's a marvellous Mediterranean feel to this simple dish.

Serves: 4

Preparation time: 10 minutes + 20 minutes cooking

Freezing: not recommended

Points per serving: 5$^1/_2$

Total Points per recipe: 22

Calories per serving: 260

1 tablespoon plain flour

1 teaspoon ground ginger

450 g (1 lb) lean shoulder or lean leg of pork, cut into cubes

1 tablespoon olive oil

2 red onions, sliced thinly (or ordinary ones)

350 g (12 oz) fine green beans, cut into short lengths

1 lemon

12 small stoned black olives

salt and freshly ground black pepper

1 tablespoon chopped fresh rosemary

1 tablespoon chopped fresh parsley

❶ Sprinkle the flour on to a plate and mix in the ground ginger. Season with salt and pepper. Roll the pork cubes in this mixture.

❷ Heat the olive oil in a large frying-pan, then add the pork and cook over a medium-high heat, stirring often, for about 8–10 minutes. Add the onions and continue to cook for 8–10 minutes more until the pork is tender and thoroughly cooked.

❸ Meanwhile, cook the green beans in a little boiling water for about 3 minutes until just tender. Drain well.

❹ Squeeze the juice from half the lemon and slice the remainder into chunks. Add the juice and lemon chunks to the frying-pan with the green beans, olives, rosemary and parsley. Cook for another minute or so and then serve on warmed plates, sprinkled with extra parsley.

Variations: instead of using fine green beans, you can use fresh asparagus when it is in season, or sliced runner beans.

Piquant Pork Stir-fry

Stir-fry strips of lean pork, egg noodles, finely sliced fresh vegetables and a few store cupboard ingredients all add up to fast, easy food with lots of flavour.

Serves: 4
Preparation and cooking time: 25 minutes
Freezing: not recommended
Points per serving: $4^1/_2$
Total Points per recipe: 18
Calories per serving: 370

175 g (6 oz) instant noodles
2 tablespoons light soy sauce
2 tablespoons seasoned rice vinegar or cider vinegar
2 tablespoons sherry
2 teaspoons sugar (dark muscovado, if possible)
2 teaspoons cornflour
1 teaspoon Chinese five-spice powder (optional)
1 tablespoon stir-fry oil or vegetable oil
350 g (12 oz) lean pork stir-fry strips
a bunch of spring onions or 1 onion, sliced
175 g (6 oz) mange-tout peas, sugar snap peas or fine green beans, sliced
1 large red pepper, de-seeded and chopped
3 celery sticks, sliced finely
salt and freshly ground black pepper

❶ Soak the noodles in boiling water for 6 minutes, or follow the packet instructions.

❷ Meanwhile, blend together the soy sauce, vinegar, sherry, sugar, cornflour and five-spice powder (if using). Set to one side.

❸ Heat the oil in a wok or a very large frying-pan. Add the pork, a handful at a time and stir-fry over a high heat for 3–4 minutes.

❹ Add the spring onions or onion, mange-tout peas, sugar snap peas or fine green beans, red pepper and celery to the pork. Stir-fry for another 3–4

minutes. Stir the soy sauce mixture and then add it to the pork and vegetables, stirring until the mixture has thickened slightly. Season to taste with salt and pepper.

❺ Drain the noodles and divide between 4 warmed serving plates. Pile the stir-fry on top and serve.

Cook's note: there are lots of different noodles in the shops for you to choose from these days. Some of them are even sold with little sachets of flavouring which will provide lots of variety for this dish.

Gammon and Vegetable Tortillas

These Mexican-style roll-ups served with chilled tomato salsa are something the whole family will enjoy.

Serves: 4

Preparation time: 10 minutes + 35 minutes cooking

Freezing: not recommended

Points per serving: 5½

Total Points per recipe: 22

Calories per serving: 490

1 tablespoon vegetable oil

1 onion, chopped

1–2 garlic cloves, crushed

175 g (6 oz) lean gammon steak, diced

1 red pepper, de-seeded and chopped

1 courgette, chopped

115 g (4 oz) mushrooms, sliced

175 g (6 oz) canned or frozen sweetcorn

1 teaspoon mild chilli powder

1 tablespoon chopped fresh coriander or parsley

4 medium (15 cm/6-inch) soft tortillas

55 g (2 oz) half-fat Cheddar cheese, grated

salt and freshly ground black pepper

a few fresh coriander sprigs or some parsley,
    to garnish

For the salsa:

150 ml (¼ pint) tomato juice

2 tomatoes, chopped finely

5 cm (2-inch) piece of cucumber, chopped finely

4 spring onions, chopped finely

1 tablespoon chopped fresh coriander

❶ Preheat the oven to Gas Mark 4/180°C/350°F.

❷ Heat the oil in a large frying-pan and sauté the onion, garlic and gammon for about 3–4 minutes. Add the red pepper, courgette, mushrooms, sweetcorn and chilli powder and cook for a few more minutes, until browned.

❸ Add the coriander or parsley to the frying-pan and mix well. Season with salt and pepper.

❹ Lay the tortillas on a work surface and divide the filling equally between them. Roll up and place in a baking dish, tucking the ends of the tortillas underneath. Scatter the grated cheese on top and bake in the oven for 20–25 minutes.

❺ Meanwhile, to make the salsa, mix together the tomato juice, tomatoes, cucumber, spring onions, and coriander. Season with salt and pepper. Chill. Serve the tortillas with the salsa, garnished with fresh coriander sprigs.

Index